GHOST TRAIN

by Roger Hurn
Illustrated by Seb Camagajevac

Titles in Ignite

Alien Sports TV	Jonny Zucker
Monster Diner	Danny Pearson
Team Games	Melanie Joyce
Mutant Baby Werewolf	Richard Taylor
Rocket Dog	Lynda Gore
The Old Lift	Alison Hawes
Spiders from Space	Stan Cullimore
Gone Viral	Mike Gould
The Ghost Train	Roger Hurn
Dog Diaries	Clare Lawrence

Badger Publishing Limited
Oldmedow Road, Hardwick Industrial Estate,
King's Lynn PE30 4JJ
Telephone: 01438 791037

www.badgerlearning.co.uk

4 6 8 10 9 7 5 3

The Ghost Train ISBN 978 1 84926 969 8

First edition © 2012
This second edition © 2014

Text © Roger Hurn 2012
Complete work © Badger Publishing Limited 2012

Publisher: Susan Ross
Senior Editor: Danny Pearson
Designer: Fiona Grant
Illustrator: Seb Camagajevac

Contents

Vocabulary:

shrugged   holograms
internet   microphone
funfair   costumes

Main characters:

Anna

Zak

Magrat

CHAPTER 1

All the fun of the fair

Zak and Anna are at the funfair.
They love going on all the thrill rides.

The Ghost Train is their favourite.
They like to save it up until last.

"Hey, Anna," said Zak. "This is a great
funfair. The Gravitron ride was
awesome."

Anna laughed. "Yes, I loved it when
you shot up in the air and yelled for
your mum!"

"Huh!" replied Zak crossly. "But what about you on the Vortex rollercoaster? It made all your hair stand up on end. You looked really weird!"

Anna sighed. Zak was right. She had looked weird, but she was not going to admit it.

"Well, at least I didn't feel sick on the Zizzler Twister," she replied. "I wanted to go on that ride again."

"That's not fair," said Zak. "The Twister didn't make me feel sick."

Anna raised her eyebrows. "Oh, really? What was it then?"

"It was the candy floss, the two hot dogs and the ice cream with fudge topping I ate for lunch."

"I told you not to have the fudge topping," said Anna. "But did you listen? No, you did not!"

Zak shrugged. "Whatever."

A big smile lit up Anna's face. "Hey, Zak," she said. "Do you know what time it is?"

Zak looked at his watch. "It's half past five," he said.

Anna shook her head. "No, it's time we went on the Ghost Train!"

Zak grinned at her. "You're right," he said. "And let's hope this Ghost Train is really scary!"

CHAPTER 2
Out of This World

Anna and Zak got on the Ghost Train.

It rumbled off into a dark tunnel. They were excited. But they were in for a big let down.

"Huh, this isn't scary at all," said Zak. "All the skeletons are made of plastic."

"They are," said Anna. "And the ghosts
are just sheets with glow-in-the-dark
paint on them."

"Oh, and that werewolf is rubbish!"
said Zak. "My gran's old poodle,
Twinks, is scarier than that."

"It is," agreed Anna. "And Twinks
hasn't even got any teeth!"

The ride made the two friends cross.

"That was the worst ghost train ride ever," said Zak. "Why don't they use holograms to make the ghost train spookier?"

"That's a great idea," said Anna. "Hey, let's make our own ghost train ride."

Zak looked puzzled. "How can we do that?"

Anna smiled. "We've got the Ghost app on our smart phones."

"Yes," said Zak. "The Ghost app projects 3D holograms of ghosts and spooks. It is just what we need!"

Anna frowned. "We have the ghosts," she said. "But we don't have the train."

Zak sighed. "Never mind," he said. "If we can't make our own ghost train we can use our phones to look up ghost trains on the internet. Then we'll find out which funfair has the best one."

They did this and then raced back to Anna's house and used her computer to double check what they'd found on their phones.

Anna soon found a website. "Hey, look at this," she said. "This funfair is called Out of This World. It says its Ghost Train is scarier than a vampire with steel fangs!"

"Wow! That is great news," said Zak.

Anna laughed. "And the even greater news is that it's coming to our town next week!"

CHAPTER 3
All aboard

The Out of This World funfair arrived.

Anna and Zak ran to see the Ghost Train.

The station looked really creepy. The tunnel was like an open mouth in a skull.

A zombie sold them their tickets.
Then a horribly hairy werewolf crept
up behind them.

It howled! Zak and Anna nearly
jumped out of their skins!

"Yay! This is more like it," whooped Zak. "This is the Ghost Train ride we want!"

"It's fab," agreed Anna. "It is really scary and we haven't even got on the train yet!"

Suddenly, the train came roaring out of the tunnel. It glowed with an unearthly light. A thick mist swirled around it.

A vampire leaned out of the driver's cab. "Who dares to climb on board?" he hissed.

"We do," shouted Zak and Anna.

But everybody else in the crowd shook their heads. "You must be joking," they said. "That train is way too spooky."

"Don't be silly," said Anna. "These guys are just actors."

"Actors with really great costumes and make-up," added Zak.

The werewolf howled again! The crowd screamed and ran off.

"What a bunch of scaredy-cats," said Zak. "It's only a fairground ride. It isn't real."

Anna nodded. "That's right. Now, come on, we don't want to miss the train."

The zombie opened the carriage door.

They jumped in. The train whistle blew. It sounded like a wailing banshee.

Then the train rolled into the mouth of the skull!

CHAPTER 4
Fear Factor

Zak and Anna loved the ride.

Ghosts and spooks screamed at them. Anna and Zak screamed back.

They shouted "BOO!" at the ghouls.

They screeched louder than the banshees. They had a brilliant time.

Suddenly, the train stopped at a station. Zak and Anna jumped out.

"What's going on?" Zak asked. "Why have we stopped here?"

"Because you have passed our Fear Factor test," said a harsh voice.

Anna and Zak spun round. A tall thin creature was standing behind them.

"Who are you?" asked Anna.

"My name is Magrat," replied the creature. "I am from the planet Tiza 3."

Anna and Zak did a double-take. "Are you an alien?" asked Zak.

Magrat nodded. "I am. And so are my friends."

The vampire, the zombie, the werewolf and all the other monsters walked onto the platform.

They took off their costumes.

"So, you guys are aliens, not actors," said Anna.

"That's right," said Magrat. "We came to Earth to find the bravest humans."

"Why did you do that?" asked Anna.

"So they can be contestants in the game show, 'Fear Factor'! It is the most popular game show on Tiza 3 TV."

"Why are you telling us this?" asked Zak.

"Because you dared to ride our scary Ghost Train," said Magrat. "So you are the winners."

Anna and Zak looked puzzled. "What have we won?" asked Zak.

Magrat smiled a nasty smile. "The trip of a lifetime to Tiza 3," she said.

Zak had a bad feeling about this.
"What will we do when we get there?"
he asked.

"You will take part in the 'Fear Factor'
game show."

"What happens in 'Fear Factor'?" asked
Anna.

Magrat smiled her nasty smile again.
"You get scared to death – for real!"

CHAPTER 5

Who are you going to call?

Anna and Zak looked at each other in horror. They had to do something fast. Then Anna had an idea.

"Do you remember how to make ghost train rides scarier?" she whispered to Zak.

Zak nodded.

"Well, now is the time to see if it works," she said.

"Stop whispering!" screeched Magrat.

"Sorry," said Anna. "But you guys are in big trouble."

Magrat stared at her. "No, you are the ones in big trouble!"

Zak shook his head. "Listen to me," he said. "You have built your Ghost Train ride on the site of an old graveyard."

"That's right," added Anna. "And the ghosts are very, very angry. They are coming to deal with you."

Magrat sneered at them. "I do not believe in ghosts."

"That is a pity," said Zak. "Because they believe in you!"

He and Anna pressed the Ghost apps on their smart phones.

The air was filled with horrible shrieks and moans. Scary monsters appeared on the platform.

They howled and screamed. Then they moved towards the aliens.

"Do something," begged Magrat. "Tell them we are sorry."

Anna shrugged. "All right," she said. "But you must promise to leave this planet now and never come back."

"We're going!" screamed Magrat. She and the aliens turned and ran for their lives.

When they had gone, Zak and Anna switched off the holograms.

"That was a close call," said Zak.

"Yes," agreed Anna. "But the aliens failed our Fear Factor test."

"They did," said Zak. "And we had the best Ghost Train ride ever!"

Famous ghosts

Many people believe that ghosts are real. The ghost of Anne Boleyn is perhaps one of the most famous in the United Kingdom. She was the second wife of King Henry VIII.

She has reportedly been seen in Hever Castle, Blickling Hall, Salle Church, Marwell Hall and most famously of all, the Tower of London. She was beheaded and it is said that some people have seen her ghost carry round its head under one of its arms.

The most famous ghosts from story books are probably the ghosts that appear in Charles Dickens' 'A Christmas Carol'. Ghosts that appear in that book are:
Jacob Marley,
The Ghost of Christmas past,
The Ghost of Christmas future,
The Ghost of Christmas yet to come.

One of the most famous ghosts which isn't human is The Flying Dutchman. The Flying Dutchman is a seventeenth-century ship that now haunts the high seas. The ship and its crew became cursed when its captain refused to take shelter in a dock during a very heavy storm. The captain dared God to sink the ship. Ever since, the ship is said to be sailing the seas for the rest of time.

Questions

What rides have Zak and Anna been on at the first funfair they visit?

What creatures can you see in the image on page 10?

Who sold Anna and Zak their tickets for the Out of This World ghost train?

What is the name of the planet that Magrat is from?

What is the name of the show that the aliens want Zak and Anna to appear on?

What is your favourite ride at a funfair or theme park?